JACK AND JILL

Jack and Jill went up the hill
To fetch a pail of water.
Jack fell down and broke his crown
And Jill came tumbling after.
Up Jack got and home did trot
As fast as he could caper.
He went to bed to mend his head
With vinegar and brown paper.

IN MEMORY OF PAT -

First published in 2011 by Hodder Children's Books

Text of activity copyright © Kate Willis-Crowley 2011
Illustrations copyright © Kate Willis-Crowley 2011

Hodder Children's Books, 338 Euston Road, London, NW1 3BH
Hodder Children's Books Australia, Level 17/207 Kent Street, Sydney,
NSW 2000

A catalogue record of this book is available from the British Library.

ISBN 978 0 340 999 78 3
10 9 8 7 6 5 4 3 2 1

Printed in China

Hodder Children's Books is a division of Hachette Children's Books,
an Hachette UK Company

www.hachette.co.uk

JACK AND JILL

Kate Willis-Crowley

A division of Hachette Children's Books

Jack and Jill went up the hill

To fetch a pail of water.

Jack fell down...

...and broke his crown,

And Jill came
tumbling after.

Up Jack got,

And home did trot,

As
fast
as he
could
caper.

He went to bed

To mend his head

with vinegar and brown paper!

HOW TO MAKE JACK AND JILL FINGER PUPPETS

TEMPLATE

YOU NEED:

Tracing paper
Card
Coloured pencils or pens
Glue
Wool for hair
Scissors and a helpful grown-up
to do the cutting.
Decorations (glitter, sequins, beads)

1 Put the tracing paper over the template
   and copy it.
2 Cut out the shape.
3 Glue the cut-out to your card.
4 Cut this out, too.
   Take extra care with the fiddly finger holes.
5 Turn it over. Now draw a Jack or Jill face
   and add arms and a t-shirt. Stick strands
   of wool to your puppet's head for hair and
   add sparkly decorations.

2

1

TEMPLATE

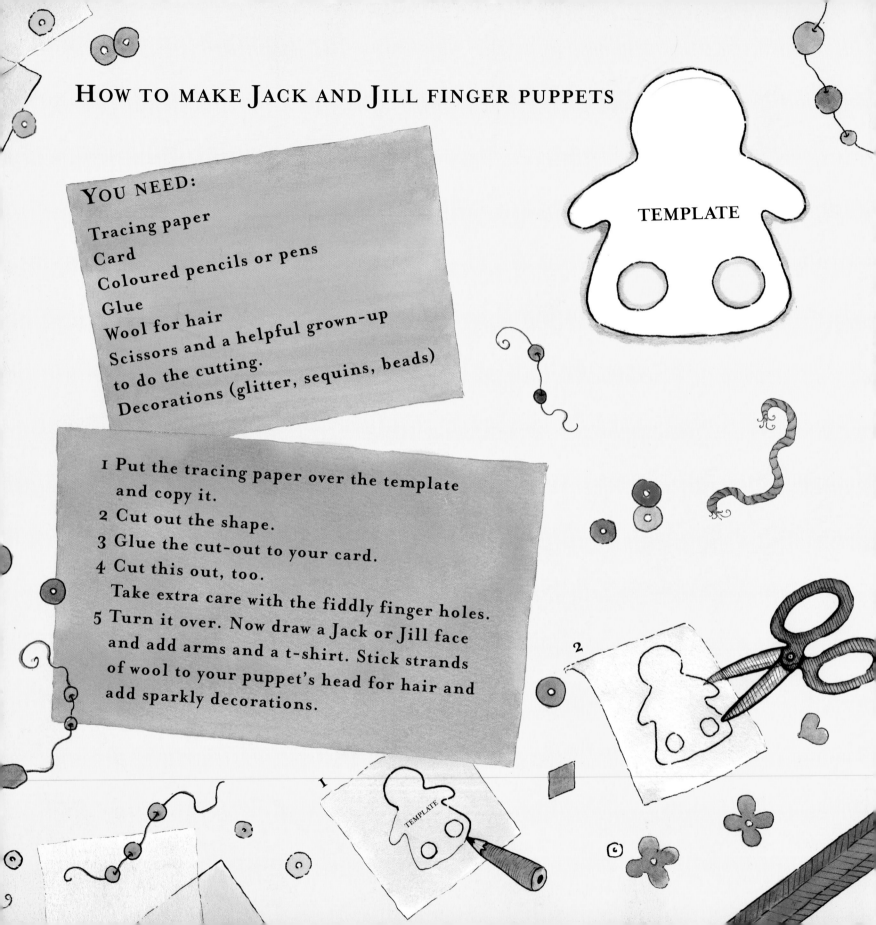

4

6 Now put two of your fingers through the holes. Your puppet is ready to play! You can make dog and kitten puppets too!

3

6

5

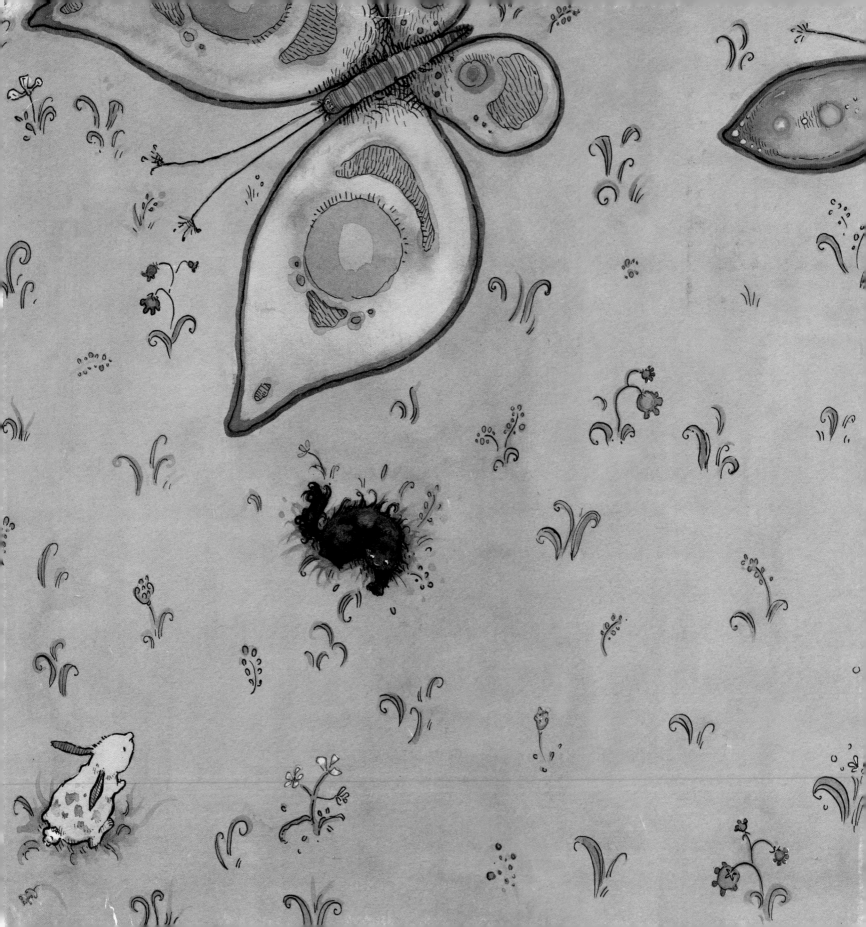